SUMMARY:

Allen Carr's Easy Way

to Stop Smoking

30 Years of Helping Smokers to Stop

ABBEY BEATHAN

Legal & Disclaimer

directly or indirectly, of any advice or information presented, whether for breach of contract, tort, negligence, personal injury, criminal intent, or under any other cause of action.

You agree to accept all risks of using the information presented inside this book. You need to consult a professional medical practitioner in order to ensure you are both able and healthy enough to participate in this program.

Table of Contents

The Book at a Glance

All smokers are aware of the fact that smoking brings about a variety of health issues, yet they can't seem to stop themselves from doing so. Even with the numerous health campaigns advocating against smoking, smokers still can't seem to stop themselves from lighting another cigarette.

In Allen Carr's Easy Way to Stop Smoking, the author provides clear and concise instructions on how a person can end his smoking habit for good. In the first chapter, he talks about his own addiction, how he was able to overcome it, and why he is determined to help others overcome the same.

In chapter two, the author introduces his readers to the Easy Method, which is his way of helping us stop smoking. It also explains why it is different from all other anti-smoking methods. Chapter three discusses the real reasons why smokers find it hard to stop. And in chapter four, the author explains why he thinks smoking is a sinister trap.

Chapter five opens our eyes to the real reasons why we can't seem to stop smoking: nicotine addiction and brainwashing. The author gave us an in-depth discussion on nicotine addiction in chapter six, while chapter seven was all about brainwashing, and how our subconscious mind affects how we perceive things.

In chapter eight, the author introduces us to the five reasons why smokers go back to lighting a cigarette as soon as they experience withdrawal pangs. These are stress, boredom, concentration, relaxation, and a combination of two, more, or all of these reasons. In chapter nine, the author digs deep into why we think we need to smoke when we feel stressed out. But more importantly, he gives us a concrete explanation on why smoking can never relieve our stress.

In chapter ten, the author explains why cigarettes make us feel tired all the time, leading to a false belief that it helps us alleviate boredom. In chapter eleven, the author shatters our false notion that smoking improves our concentration, while in chapter nine, he shares why he thinks smokers are the most unrelaxed individuals on the planet. And finally, chapter thirteen will be a brief explanation as to why smokers think combination cigarettes are the best – and why, in reality, it is the worst.

Chapter fourteen and fifteen makes it clear that when we give up smoking, we don't lose anything. But instead, we gain everything. In chapters sixteen to twenty one, the author provides us with a thorough discussion on how smoking affects our budget, health, energy, and confidence. Chapters 22 to 24 introduces us to the traditional anti-smoking methods, and provides us with explanations as to why they don't work. And finally, chapter 25 to 27 provides us with a breakdown of the different types of smokers.

Beginning from chapter 28 until chapter 31, the author discusses the important factors that we must consider before proceeding with the Easy Way. In chapter 32, the author lays down the two steps involved in the easy method: to commit and to develop a mindset of rejoicing. Chapters 33 to 38 sufficiently provides us with tips and pieces of advice which will help us get through the dreaded withdrawal period.

The breathtakingly beautiful moment of revelation is discussed in chapter 39. And finally, the last part of this book contains final pieces of advice to help us get through the post-withdrawal phase.

Thus, as long as we carefully and consciously follow the instructions laid down in this book, we can be certain that we can finally put an end to our smoking problem. And better yet, we can also serve as an inspiration to others who are also experiencing the same problem.

Introduction

No addiction is untreatable. However, those who suffer from vices tend to believe otherwise – as a result, that belief would prevent them from completely letting go of their nasty ways.

Allen Carr was among those who believed that there was no way out of his chain-smoking ways. He shares that he has tried a lot, if not all, of today's anti-smoking methods. Unfortunately, all of his efforts went down the drain since he would fall back to smoking within months.

Through the author's determination to get rid of this nasty habit, coupled with the support from his wife and loved ones, the author was able to discover the Easy Way out of smoking. To make sure that his method works for everyone, he tried it out with friends first. After receiving their positive feedback, he became determined to share it with the world. And that is the main purpose of this book.

Nonetheless, the author understands that some readers will be skeptic about what he is about to present – after all, most of his readers are the ones who have also failed to escape their slavery to nicotine. But to be truly free, we have to start somewhere. And fortunately, you already took the first step when you picked up this book.

The Worst Nicotine Addict I Have Yet to Meet

Before discussing the main points of the Easy Way, the author wants his readers to understand where he's coming from first.

In this chapter, his shares that he used to be a chain smoker for around thirty years, and that he has already tried all of the known means to get rid of this habit – and all of them to no avail. In fact, he was already on the brink of giving up when his wife encouraged him to see a hypnotherapist.

Despite his skepticism, he still decided to push through with it. Fortunately, the result was promising. He shares that he immediately stopped smoking after the session, and didn't have a hard time during the withdrawal stage.

Nonetheless, he reminds us that hypnotherapy isn't the ultimate answer to end smoking. Since it treats people by suggesting messages, we must be careful with the kind of message that is being sent our way. Otherwise, we can never be free from the smoking trap. Eventually, this led the author to discover the Easy Way to stop smoking.

Throughout reading this book, the author wants us to keep an open mind. After all, quitting itself is easy. The real challenge lies in getting past the withdrawal stage. Fortunately, this book will provide us with clear and concrete instructions on how we can move past that stage.

The Easy Method

Most anti-smoking methods fail because they encourage us to stop smoking at the onset, and then leave us with a strong sense of craving towards getting back on board. In contrast, the method in this book aims to help us develop a mindset first – a mindset that we're already free from the chains of nicotine. And from this, we can gather the strength to actually put an end to smoking.

In order to develop this mindset, we must reflect on the following questions first:

- What is smoking doing to me?

- Am I actually enjoying it?

- Is it necessary for me to keep on smoking throughout my life?

These questions should be enough to give us a wakeup call that smoking does nothing good to our body. Nonetheless, the author acknowledges that there can also be smokers who would try to provide rationalized answers to justify their situation. But if we analyze their answers, we begin to realize that their reasons are all illusions and false beliefs.

Thus, in order to get to the bottom of a person's smoking

problems, we must first debunk these fallacies and illusions. Once these are removed from a person's life, he can now focus on the things that truly matter in his life.

Why is it Difficult to Stop?

It may not be obvious, but the fact remains that all smokers wish to quit. They are all aware of the negative effects of smoking, and that terrifies them enough to want to break the habit as soon as possible. The author even shares that a common desire among confirmed smokers is to go back in time to stop themselves from enjoying that first cigarette.

But, despite knowing the hazards of smoking, they can't seem to stop themselves from lighting another cigarette. Quitting is just too difficult.

In order to stop smoking, we must understand why it is so hard to stop in the first place. Numerous organizations campaign against smoking by explaining how and why it is easy to stop. However, these campaigns often fail and cause smokers to fall back to their horrible ways.

In contrast, the Easy Way will help us understand why quitting is hard. The author wants us to understand that our reasons for smoking are all just illusions. He explains each illusion as follows:

- Quitting can create a stronger withdrawal symptom. In a succeeding chapter, we will understand that actual withdrawal symptoms from nicotine are not as powerful as what we have imagined.

- Smoking is enjoyable. There are other things we enjoy, but we never take these other things excessively.

- There are deep psychological reasons. Some people only resort to smoking because they want to exude an image of maturity. Unfortunately, that is not always the result they get.

- Smoking makes a person look macho. Breathing cancerous tars into your system isn't manly at all.

- Smoking relieves boredom. Keep in mind that boredom is only a frame of mind. Besides, there is nothing truly interesting about lighting a cigarette.

- I smoke because my friends smoke. You don't have to do what others are doing. After all, you are the only person in control of your own life.

- Smoking has already become a habit, and habits are hard to break. This is a fallacy. The author shares that in the United Kingdom, drivers formed the habit of driving on the left lane – but they can easily break that habit if they have to drive in countries where right-lane driving is observed.

With all these fallacies and illusions debunked, we can now embrace the real reason why it is so hard to stop smoking: we are addicted to nicotine.

Once we come to fully understand that the real problem is an addiction, dealing with it would be easier. In fact, the author shares that we can fully let go of smoking within three weeks' time.

The Sinister Trap

Smoking is a sinister trap that's hard to escape once you're inside. We are often lured into it because we see smoking adults who always warn us against how disgusting a cigarette is. But since they can't seem to stop smoking, it's hard to believe that they're not enjoying it – and that makes us curious enough to give it a try.

Now, how hooked we become to smoking all depends on that first cigarette. If it tastes awful, then we can confirm to ourselves that we don't enjoy it. We never become hooked. On the other hand, if that first puff tastes amazing, then we've already entered the trap.

The author goes on to add that we only want to exit this smoking trap when life begins to feel more stressful because of it. But as soon as we quit, we experience more stress because we're no longer allowed to depend on that one thing that seems to help us relieve it. And within a span of a few days, we finally give in. We light a cigarette and firmly decide to quit when we're no longer under extreme amounts of stress. Unfortunately, that day never arrives.

But like what has been discussed in the previous chapter, all of this is just an illusion. Keep in mind that no matter how complicated a puzzle may be, it always has a corresponding solution. And this sinister smoking trap is no different.

Why Do We Carry on Smoking?

With all the negative effects of smoking in mind, any logical person would wonder why smokers find it hard to quit. However, smokers are smart and rational individuals. They are aware of all these health risks. They are also aware of how much money they are spending on cigarettes in a year. There's no need to remind them of all of these.

Instead, we must discuss and understand the real reasons why they can't seem to stop. According to the author, there are only two main reasons: nicotine addiction and brainwashing. Each of these reasons will be discussed in detail in the two succeeding chapters.

Nicotine Addiction

Now that we are aware of our true situation, we have to dig deeper into what this nicotine addiction is.

Nicotine is a colorless, oily, and highly addictive compound found in tobacco. When nicotine enters our lungs and into our veins, it provides us with an illusion that it is pleasurable. But this compound immediately leaves the bloodstream within minutes, and that makes the smoker feel withdrawal symptoms.

But at this point, the author wants to make one thing clear with us: these withdrawal pangs are mainly mental. In other words, the pangs you think you feel are all in your head. Unfortunately, the addiction tricks us to think that it's all real.

With these facts in mind, we may still find it hard to believe that we are addicted to nicotine. Fortunately, nicotine is not like other drugs – it is easy to kick out of our system. But before we can do that, we must first accept that we are, in fact, addicted to it.

Accepting that we're nicotine addicts can be hard to swallow. To help us ease into that thought, the author shares the following reasons why acceptance can help us overcome our main problem:

1. We do not see the cigarette as a prop, but as something we actually enjoy. If we accept that we are addicted to it, coupled with the realization that smoking is bad for our health, our eyes become open to reality.

2. Once we accept that we are addicted, we can immediately proceed with getting rid of the nicotine in our body. According to studies, this only takes about three weeks, regardless of how heavy or how long you have been smoking.

Nonetheless, our problem doesn't end with acknowledging our nicotine addiction. According to the author, the real problem lies in being brainwashed by the little nicotine monster. More on brainwashing will be discussed in the succeeding chapter.

11

Brainwashing and the Sleeping Partner

From everything that has been discussed in the previous chapter, we now come to understand that nicotine addiction stems from brainwashing. In this chapter, the author gives us an in-depth explanation of brainwashing, and how our sleeping partner plays a vital role in it.

Our subconscious mind, which the author refers to as the Sleeping Partner, has a lot to do with our nicotine addiction. The author explains that the power of suggestion plays a starring role in convincing the subconscious mind to make us do something. Unfortunately, advertising and marketing companies know exactly how to use it – and this is exactly what is employed by companies selling cigarette.

Additionally, movies and television shows often portray smokers as confident, macho, and sociable individuals, and this effectively lures us to try smoking. Sometimes, the brainwashing can also stem from our own homes, especially if we have a role model who smokes.

But as early as now, the author wants us to keep in mind that all of these are mere illusions. Smoking only introduces filth and nicotine into our lungs, and that doesn't solve any of our problems. It can't magically transform us into the person we've always wanted to become, and neither can it effectively reduce our stress levels.

Understanding and embracing the fact that we are being brainwashed into smoking can make this process easier than it already is. As long as we continuously remind ourselves that the joys of smoking are all mere illusions, then we remain on the path towards freedom from nicotine slavery.

Relieving Withdrawal Pangs

Back in the early days, when the cigarette was first introduced to society, it was merely considered as a social prop. What people didn't know then was that a single cigarette could subtly lure them towards an addiction that is hard to break free from.

Most smokers tend to believe that the more drawn we become to nicotine, the stronger the withdrawal pangs would become. However, the truth is that withdrawal symptoms from nicotine are so subtle, that smokers only realize that they are addicted to it when they try to stop smoking.

Among the many reasons why smokers go back to smoking after trying to stop is the belief that it helps reduce stress, alleviate boredom, improve concentration, boost relaxation, or a combination of all of these. In the succeeding chapters, the author aims to disprove all of these beliefs.

Stress

The biggest reason why people turn to smoking is the belief that it can reduce their stress levels. To disprove this notion, the author provides us with an illustration.

He shares that for some people, a telephone conversation can be stressful, especially for a businessman who may receive calls from dissatisfied customers, or from his infuriated boss. Because of his anxiety he ends up lighting a cigarette. He doesn't really know why he does it, but it seems to make him feel relieved.

On the contrary, the author explains that the businessman was already experiencing withdrawal pangs, which seems to have aggravated his normal stress levels. By smoking, he relieved his withdrawal stress, which also gives him an illusion that his stress levels went down. Unfortunately, the more a person lights a cigarette, the more stressed he actually becomes, compared to a non-smoker. The author explains this by saying that with every puff of the cigarette, the nicotine becomes less effective in restoring a person's stress levels.

Now, to help us get into the proper mindset, he wants us to visualize that our doctor finally tells us that if we don't stop smoking, he will have to remove our legs. After hearing this, pause for a while and imagine what life would be like without legs. A logical mind would easily choose to give up smoking. But, the heaviest smokers would simply dismiss this visualization and still proceed with smoking. This is what this drug can do to us: it can take away our nerve and courage. It can make us believe that it is our source of strength when, in reality, it is the one that's taking our life away.

So today, make sure to reflect on the fact that the cigarette is not responsible for calming our nerves. Instead, keep on reminding yourself that it is the very reason which is causing our nerves to deteriorate. Once we do so, we regain our confidence and self-assurance, without being dependent on any drug.

Boredom

Boredom is another reason why some people end up smoking. But as previously stated, boredom is a frame of mind. It cannot be alleviated by intoxicating yourself with harmful substances.

The author shares that when we stop smoking, even for just a few minutes, we would feel as if something is missing. If we're busy, we barely realize that we are experiencing withdrawal from the absence of that drug. On the contrary, if we're not doing anything, we end up feeding the nicotine monster.

Additionally, the author also wants to point out that cigarettes can even increase our boredom, since it makes us feel tired – and this makes us lose interest in any other activity. From this, we can see a cycle of lighting a cigarette, feeling bored as a result, and then lighting another cigarette under the false belief that it can alleviate boredom. From the standpoint of a non-smoker, or an ex-chain smoker, nothing is more boring than that of lighting a cigarette over and over again.

Concentration

Another thing we have to hammer into our heads is this: cigarettes do not, and cannot, help improve our concentration.

In reality, we end up lighting a cigarette because the nicotine monster keeps on nagging us to be fed. As soon as he gets his share of the drug, the nicotine monster allows us proceed with what we have to do – that is, until he needs another dose of it.

From this, we can now see that smoking does not improve our concentration at all. If anything, it is actually ruining it. Recall that the more we intoxicate ourselves with nicotine, the less relieved we become over time. Thus, it only makes our situation worse.

Additionally, nicotine blocks our arteries and veins, which makes it difficult to supply the brain with oxygen. As a result, our concentration becomes adversely affected. According to the author, this is the reason why some of the willpower methods don't work. After all, how could a person possibly will himself to stop smoking if the nicotine monster keeps blocking out his concentration?

Before ending this chapter, the author wants us to know that there are no physical withdrawal pangs. Everything is in our heads. If we believe that smoking improves our concentration, then why are there non-smokers who demonstrate great levels of concentration? Ponder on that. Usually, it's the self-doubt that makes it hard to let go.

Relaxation

Smoking does not help anyone relax. In fact, the author shares that nicotine can even make our pulse rate higher.

From what the author has gathered, he can confidently tell us that the most unrelaxed people are those who smoke. If you try to look around, you will notice that smokers are the ones who would easily lose their temper and throw a fit. Unfortunately, the sad part is that they rarely think that there is anything wrong with them.

The author goes on to add that smoking actually tends to rob people of feeling joy. When they think they're beginning to relax because of the cigarette, it is actually the nicotine monster that's calmed down – not you. As soon as you're done with one stick, the monster would want to have another one, and you'll feel agitated all over again. Thus, only non-smokers are capable of experiencing true relaxation.

Combination Cigarettes

According to the author, we resort to combination cigarettes when we experience two, more, or all of the reasons for smoking in one occasion. When we smoke during these situations, we think that it is the only way for us to really enjoy the event and feel relaxed.

Again, everything is all in our heads. However, this is also the type which we think we'll miss most if we have to stop smoking. In our heads, we think that it is something we cannot let go of, since it can drastically improve our lives with just one cigarette.

But that is all an illusion. Keep in mind that the cigarette is only relieving us from withdrawal symptoms. The moment we stopped smoking, we began to feel overwhelmed by pangs of withdrawal, so we are made to believe that the cigarette offered a cure. But in reality, the occasion wasn't as stressful as we thought it was – it was the nicotine monster which made it seem worse.

To let go, we must change our perspective of the combination cigarette. There is absolutely nothing special about it. Instead of helping us enjoy the occasion, we end up less focused on it because the nicotine monster keeps nudging us to go out and smoke. As a result, this makes the event seem stressful, so we never really end up enjoying it.

What Am I Giving up?

To a chain smoker, quitting would feel like giving up everything. But in reality, we are not giving up anything at all. And in return, we gain everything.

Before beginning with this chapter's discussion, the author wants us to keep on reminding ourselves that cigarettes do not fill a void in our lives. On the contrary, they are responsible for creating those voids in the first place.

To explain how smoking creates a void, the author shares that when we smoke during social events, we often think it helps us become more confident and sociable. However, keep in mind that no one really likes the smell of cigarettes. As a result, you try your best to keep the smoke away from the person you're talking to, while also making sure that you dispose of the ash in a manner that won't cause such a mess. The stained teeth and the bad breath doesn't help, either.

Thus, there really is nothing to lose if we give up on smoking. Keep this in mind when you are tempted to light another cigarette.

Self-imposed Slavery

It may be hard to admit, but we are responsible for our own slavery to nicotine. The author shares that most smokers don't usually like their first cigarette, but the brainwashing is so strong, that they end up trying it a second or third time. Unfortunately, by this time, the body now gets a kick from the nicotine, and the slavery starts.

The interesting part about cigarette smoking, however, is that the smoker usually doesn't realize that he is already addicted – that is, until he is forced not to smoke. For example, a smoker may find it stressful when he visits a friend's home, and find that there is no ash tray. This is also the case when he has to socialize with people who are disgusted by the smell of smoke. Because he feels deprived, he becomes agitated and irritable.

From a logical standpoint, not being allowed to smoke shouldn't agitate us. In fact, we should be thankful. However, smokers no longer think that way because the nicotine monster already have them enslaved.

I'll Save £x a Week

Smokers who are doing well in life aren't usually bothered by a slight increase in the price of a pack of cigarette. A pack is usually worth a few bucks, and this doesn't mean anything to an established individual earning thousands per month.

However, if we are to compute the amount they will be spending for a lifetime supply of cigarette, it would cost them up to around £40,000! Unfortunately, smokers rarely realize how much their spending on cigarettes because they never think of it as something they would be dealing with forever – that is, until you try to make them stop smoking.

Thus, the author often tries to make smokers compute how much money he'll be spending on cigarettes if he wouldn't stop today. Once the smoker realizes that the amount is too substantial to be thrown away like that, he will be determined to stop smoking.

Health

Everyone is aware of the health hazards that go hand in hand with smoking. However, bear in mind that smokers are being brainwashed to think that smoking is good for them, so they may not fully comprehend the gravity of its health risks.

The brainwashing is so strong that smokers would rather try to live with much precaution – like making sure that they won't get hit by a bus as they cross the road – but they fail to realize that the bigger threat on their life lies in the fact that they smoke. They become extra keen on making sure that they won't get into physical accidents, and yet they try to poison themselves every day.

Unfortunately, most smokers only consider this as a harmless habit. This is especially true when they don't experience symptoms like coughing yet. But according to the author, the tar from nicotine rarely triggers any symptoms – they just build up in our lungs and become cancer.

Thus, the next time we light a cigarette, think of it as lighting a fuse. The more you light it, the closer the bomb is to exploding. Are you really willing to risk it?

Energy

Another effect of brainwashing is that smokers don't often realize that smoking has taken its toll on their energy levels.

From a scientific standpoint, smoking fills our lungs with tar, which makes us inhale less oxygen. As a result, our brain gets deprived of oxygen and other nutrients, and that can make us lose focus and feel tired all the time. Unfortunately, most smokers think that their constant lack of energy is only due to the fact that they are no longer energetic children.

According to the author, the opposite is true. As we age, we can have the same levels of energy as when we were children. It is only the nicotine monster that is making us feel tired all the time. In fact, he even shares that as soon as he extinguished his last cigarette, he already felt a big impact on his health. He no longer experienced an asthma attack, and his breathing has become less congested. And soon enough, he was able to jog and swim again.

It Relaxes Me and Gives Me Confidence

The author wants to remind us that smoking does not help us relax, and neither does it provide us with a confidence boost. In fact, it can even leave us feeling insecure, especially when we find ourselves running out of cigarettes in the middle of the night.

Thus, the next time we feel the need to smoke in order to relax, we must remind ourselves that we are only being brainwashed. We are only feeding the nicotine monster who is only wreaking havoc inside our body.

Those Sinister Black Shadows

All smokers have a reason for wanting to quit. Among the most common reasons are health and finances. But for the author, one of the biggest reasons would be to get rid of the sinister black shadows that were always lurking at the back of his mind.

According to the author, these sinister black shadows stem from the feeling of being despised by non-smokers. He shares that smokers are aware that people are disgusted by the smell of cigarettes, so they know how displeased non-smokers can be when they see others smoking in public. Because of this, the author also began to feel apologetic towards non-smokers, because he couldn't seem to stop smoking.

Fortunately, he was able to discover the Easy Way, and he was finally able to get rid of these sinister black shadows. Accordingly, this made the biggest impact in his life. He even claims that getting rid of these shadows made him respect himself a lot more.

The Advantages of Being a Smoker

This chapter literally contains nothing – because there really is nothing to gain from being a smoker.

The Willpower Method of Stopping

Smokers often think that they can simply will themselves to stop smoking. However, this method usually fails because we are no longer in control of our own mind. We are now slaves to the nicotine monster.

Additionally, the author also adds that the problem lies in the fact that it takes us too long to recognize that we are already addicted. Smokers who only light up a cigarette or two per day would even laugh at the suggestion. However, if we were to completely take their cigarettes away from them, they'll soon realize that they can't seem to give it up that easily.

Much of the problem with the Willpower Method also lies in the fact that smokers were already brainwashed to think that it smoking is enjoyable. This is the biggest reason why smokers fall back to their old ways during the infamous withdrawal period. But again, this is all just part of an illusion. There is nothing enjoyable about feeding our body with poison.

Fortunately, all this brainwashing only occurs as long as the nicotine monster lives within us. It ends when it is completely flushed out of our system. According to the author, this can last for about three weeks. And the better news is that his Easy Way can help get us through this dreaded period.

Beware of Cutting Down

A majority of smokers believe that cutting down on his cigarette consumption is a great way to eventually end his addiction. However, this can actually make the addiction grow worse.

According to the author, cutting down is bad for smokers because of the following reasons:

1. He is still keeping the nicotine monster alive.

2. Cutting down means that he is desperately waiting for the next time he can smoke, and that is not a good use of his time.

3. This can double his suffering. He deals with life's normal stresses and responsibilities, while also trying to deal with the nicotine monster he's been feeding.

4. On average, smokers who try to cut down end up smoking even more. Lighting and smoking cigarettes became automatic, so they barely realize that they have already finished an entire pack.

Thus, instead of cutting down, the author wants us to fully commit to stop smoking. Reducing our intake will not make it easier for us to stop at all, so there's no point to doing it gradually. All it takes to stop is getting the right frame of mind. More on this topic will be discussed on a later chapter.

Just One Cigarette

All it took for smokers to become hooked is one cigarette. That one cigarette catapulted them into this addiction, and now they find it impossible to escape from the trap.

Every day, the smoker struggles with his promise to smoke just one cigarette. Unfortunately, that one cigarette often starts a chain, which leaves him smoking twenty more cigarettes for the entire day.

Thus, whenever we feel tempted to smoke just one cigarette, the author wants us to think of the lifetime of misery that that one cigarette is going to take us to. Would it be worth it?

To end this chapter, the author lays down the following fundamentals that we should keep in mind:

1. There is nothing to lose if we give up on smoking. Instead, we gain a multitude of advantages.

2. The odd cigarette is just a myth. It does not exist. On the contrary, what exists is a lifetime of poisoning yourself.

3. All smokers, even when one thinks that he is already a hopeless case, can find it easy to stop smoking.

Casual Smokers, Teenagers, Non-smokers

In this chapter, the author wishes to present us with some noteworthy definitions.

- Non-smokers. These are defined as those who were never lured into the sinister trap. Nonetheless, these non-smokers should not be complacent.

- Casual smokers. According to the author, there are two basic classifications of casual smokers: those who have fallen into the trap but doesn't realize it yet, and those who were former heavy smokers. The author goes on to list down other classifications of smokers under this category, like those who only smoke five cigarettes per day, those who only smoke during the morning or evening, and those who believe that they are merely occasional smokers.

The author believes that those who classify themselves as casual smokers are in the same trouble as those who are heavy smokers. They are trapped in the same puzzle, after all. But to get them to stop, they must first realize that they are already addicted.

The same warning goes for the occasional smoker who thinks that he doesn't like smoking at all. According to the author, all heavy smokers began as occasional smokers. Thus, if the occasional smoker really thinks that he doesn't like it, then he should give up on smoking all at once.

This chapter ends with a warning for parents to not be complacent in raising their children. If they see that children are disgusted by the smell of cigarette, that doesn't automatically mean that they will grow up as non-smokers. They should make sure that there will be no place for brainwashing as they grow up, especially when they become teenagers. After all, teenagers are the hardest to convince that they need treatment, especially when they are filled with that youthful energy and health.

The Secret Smoker

The Secret Smoker falls under a special category. According to the author, these are the smokers who were banned from smoking, but their craving is so strong so they look for ways to smoke without being caught.

This kind of smoker will find ways just so they can get a taste of the cigarette. The author shares that when he used to be a secret smoker, he would mindlessly cause an argument just so he can storm out of the house and light a smoke. On other occasions, he would volunteer to buy a minor item, take a smoking break, and then return home hours later. It was so obvious that he was trying to sneak a smoke, and it ended up making him feel a little antisocial.

Looking back on his experiences, the author also recalls how restless he was during that phase. He was constantly worrying that his wife would find his hidden stash of cigarette. He was in constant fear that he would reek of the smell of cigarette. Eventually, this caused him to lose his self-respect. And he doesn't want this to happen to you.

A Social Habit?

A common myth surrounding cigarette smoking is that it is a social habit. However, the opposite is true. Smokers themselves admit that they find it rather antisocial.

With the help of mass media and information technology, more and more people are becoming aware of the hazards of smoking and inhaling second-hand smoke. This makes non-smokers loathe those who smoke in public, and smokers end up feeling guilty and apologetic. As a result, they try not to smoke during social events, and this only leaves them feeling deprived. This causes smokers to scurry off to a distance where they can be away from people and smoke in peace.

For most smokers, this is enough reason for them to give up on smoking completely. And fortunately, an increasing number of smokers are quitting on a daily basis. Do you really want to be the last one to stay on a sinking ship?

Timing

Having the determination to finally stop smoking is a noble gesture. However, there is also another factor that we must take into consideration: timing.

This doesn't mean that we have to find the right time when we should quit. If we do so, then the answer would obviously be "now".

However, all the brainwashing is making us believe that the right time to quit is when we are not too stressed. But let's get real: all of us experience stress on a daily basis. When we promise to quit when we're no longer stressed, it's like we're making a promise to never quit at all.

Thus, the author wants us to fight off the brainwashing. There is no perfect timing for quitting. We have to quit now.

Will I Miss the Cigarette?

The answer to this question is a resounding "no".

The author guarantees that as soon as we kill off that little monster and successfully flush it out of our system, then we would be free from any form of temptation. After all, we all know how horrible smoking is, so the only logical explanation for all that craving is that it is the work of the nicotine monster.

Additionally, the author wants us to remember that smokers don't deserve our envy. Think about it: smokers consume thousands of pounds a year on something that is poisoning them. Do we really want to envy someone who lives like that? Absolutely not. If anything, we should pity them instead.

Will I Put on Weight?

This is another myth that the author wishes to bust. Keep in mind that smoking drains our confidence, health, and energy. Once we get rid of it, then we can regain all of these back. If we are able to regain our energy, then we can easily adapt an active lifestyle.

Additionally, the author adds that this constant worrying over our weight stems from the fact that the smoking made us insecure. As soon as we get rid of the nicotine monster, then that insecurity will go away. In exchange, we get our confidence and self-respect back.

In succeeding chapter, the author will introduce us to the Easy Way to Stop Smoking. If we carefully follow the instructions, then he can guarantee that weight gain is nothing to worry about.

Avoid False Incentives

Some smokers try to use the Willpower Method coupled with false incentives to try to get them out of this horrible habit. But more often than not, this usually fails.

For example, someone would claim to stop buying cigarettes and save the money he so that he could buy himself a new gadget, or go on vacation with his family. The author explains that this usually fails because the incentive is false. The smoker doesn't really feel the pressure to quit smoking with that incentive. And since there is no real pressure to stop, he wouldn't feel bad about breaking the promise. Soon enough, he's back to smoking packs of cigarette a day.

Thus, if we want to stop smoking, we must really want to do it. There is no need for incentives and bribes. The mere fact that smoking offers nothing should be enough to make us quit.

The Easy Way to Stop

By now, we're finally ready for the Easy Way to stop smoking. According to the author, there are only two things we have to do. First, we must finally make the decision to quit; and second, we must not sulk about it. Instead, we should rejoice that we can finally be free from nicotine.

To prepare ourselves for the first step, the author wants to keep these pointers in mind:

- You are capable of achieving it. The only person in control of your own acts and thoughts is yourself. Thus, realize that the only person who can make you light another cigarette – or stop doing so – is yourself.

- There is nothing to lose. When we give up smoothing, we're not giving up anything we love. In return, we end up gaining so much.

- There is no such thing as one cigarette. The author explains that smoking is an addiction to a certain drug – nicotine – and one cigarette can cause another chain reaction.

- Smoking is a drug addiction, and not a sociable habit.

Face the fact that you are addicted, and that the longer you run away from the cure, the worse you would become. Choose to face the cure today.

- Remember that the first moment you choose to stop smoking, you are already a non-smoker. Dwell on the fact that you are no longer a smoker, and rejoice in it. This will help you appreciate and enjoy life a whole lot more.

Once you have finally set your mind to finally quit smoking, there is a tendency to feel gloomy. This is all part of the process. The author explains that this unhappiness stems from the following:

- You have not fully embraced the abovementioned pointers. Give yourself time to believe and embrace each of the statements above.

- You fear failure. Remind yourself that you will succeed, and that any confidence trick wouldn't work on you because you are an intelligent person.

- You feel miserable about quitting, even if you believe all of the abovementioned pointers. Think about quitting as finally escaping prison – it is something to be happy about. Focus on that feeling of triumph.

Through these tips, the author guarantees that we would be able to develop the frame of mind necessary for the first step. Once we have finally decided to stop smoking, all that's necessary is to maintain that frame of mind throughout the withdrawal period. More on this will be discussed in the next chapter

But, before ending this chapter, the author issues the following warnings:

- As much as possible, he advises us to plan to fully put an end to smoking after finishing this book.

- The withdrawal period can last about three weeks. Make sure that your frame of mind is set to, "It's marvelous that I am never going to smoke again!" instead of, "I can survive three weeks without smoking". These statements can make a big difference.

The Withdrawal Period

Within three weeks after deciding to have a final cigarette, we should expect to experience withdrawal symptoms. According to the author, this may not only be caused by the withdrawal from nicotine, but may also be due to other psychological triggers from the stressors around us.

Again, the author reminds us that there is no physical pain during this period. If you think you're under physical pain, think again – it's highly likely that it's all in your head. The author shares that some smokers claim to experience hunger or stomach rumblings during this period. More often than not, it's the little nicotine monster that's actually hungry, not you.

To the heaviest smokers, this may be his most miserable period. When you experience this, keep on reminding yourself that there is nothing to be sad about. After all, you're not giving up anything. This decision will benefit you in so many ways, so why are you still moping about it? It is also necessary to remind ourselves that this feeling of unhappiness, if not countered at the onset, will only trigger the brainwashing process to start all over again.

During this period, it is necessary to keep on reminding yourself that cigarettes do nothing to help you. It is merely a prop. It cannot make occasions more sociable, neither does it complete a meal. It is not pleasurable at all. In fact, the only reason you crave it is due to a drug, nicotine. Make sure to reflect on these facts so that they can be gelled into your head eventually.

Nonetheless, the author doesn't want us to completely forget about smoking. This exercise isn't about forgetting how to smoke at all. Instead, it is all about embracing the joys of never having to smoke again. After months or years of being chained to nicotine, you are finally free from it!

And finally, regardless of what you experience during this period, the most important thing is to never doubt your decision. As soon as you let an inkling of doubt cloud your thoughts, it will start a chain of negative emotions, which will ultimately defeat the purpose. As much as possible, focus on the wonderful reasons why you should stop smoking. Rejoice over the fact that you are no longer a prisoner to the nicotine monster. Most importantly, remember that this period is only temporary. Soon enough, you will just come to realize that you are no longer craving a smoke.

Just One Puff

During the withdrawal period, we may be tempted to take one or two puffs off of a cigarette. Sure, that first puff won't taste good anymore, so we may think that we're finally losing interest. However, the author shares that the opposite is true.

He reminds us that since we've been starving the nicotine monster for days or weeks already, just one puff would be enough to make it strong again – and send you flying back to square one. We all began with one puff, after all.

To keep our minds off of taking another puff, the author reminds us that doing so has two damaging effects. The first is that it keeps the monster alive, and the second is that it helps the monster convince us to take more puffs.

Thus, we shouldn't fall for the temptation of just one puff. Redirect your attention to the joys of being nicotine-free.

Will It Be Harder for Me?

The author notes that there will be times when we might think that the withdrawal period is harder on us than on others. After all, each of us have different circumstances, professions, and interests. We may think that some of us may have it easier because they're not under constantly high levels of stress on a daily basis.

More particularly, the author is sure that smokers from the medical profession would find the withdrawal difficult hard because of the following reasons:

- Their awareness of health risks creates fear.

- Their work is highly stressful.

- They feel guilty because they should be setting an example to others.

All these factors amplify his feeling of being deprived of what his body thinks is an escape from all his problems.

According to the author, these are all reminders from the nicotine monster that we have already stopped smoking. Instead of worrying and amplifying the negative emotions, we should rejoice that we are no longer under its control. It may seem hard, but the key is to develop a frame of mind that will unceasingly remind us to rejoice. Thus, regardless of age, profession, sex, or intelligence, as long as we have already developed that frame of mind, the author guarantees that we will find this process relatively easy.

The Main Reasons for Failure

According to the author, there are only two reasons to fail in this method: the influence of others, and having a bad day.

The first reason usually occurs during occasions and gatherings, where a companion would light up a cigarette. This situation can be especially tempting during our weakest moments. However, this wouldn't be a problem if we have already developed the rejoicing mindset. Thus, instead of sulking or feeling deprived, focus on the fact that you are no longer a prisoner of the nicotine monster. Besides, maybe you can inspire your friend to do the same.

The second reason for failure is having bad days, and thinking that smoking can make it better. However, we now know that smoking doesn't really help us relax – in fact, it can even make us more restless than we already are. When this happens to us, the author wants us to remember that everyone has bad days, whether he's a smoker or not, but non-smokers tend to cope with bad days better. The author goes on to explain that smoking will only cause us to feed the nicotine monster, without solving any of the real reasons why we're having a bad day.

Thus, we can easily triumph over these reasons for failure if we always keep a positive mindset.

Substitutes

At this point, the author wants to warn us against substitutes like chewing gum, herbal cigarettes, and pills. These substitutes are often encouraged an anti-smoking method, and are sometimes recommended by therapists and doctors. However, they do not solve the smoking problem; instead, they can make our situation worse.

For this chapter, the author wants us to remember these key points:

1. Nicotine has no substitute;

2. Nicotine is poison, so we don't need it in our body;

3. Cigarettes create voids instead of filling them.

From these pointers, it is clear that we must avoid substitutes which also contain nicotine, like gum, nasal spray, and patches. These substitutes contain the same amount of nicotine, which only add fuel to the addiction. After all, we cannot solve a drug problem by taking in the same drug – or any drug, for that matter.

During these times, we must remember that the real problem is the brainwashing. We're not really experiencing physical withdrawal pains – this illusion is simply created by the nicotine monster so that we may be lured into feeding it.

Thus, think of your withdrawal symptoms as your body's way of telling you that it is finally getting rid of all the nicotine in your system. Instead of moping about it, enjoy the fact that you are on your way to freedom and being poison-free.

Should I Avoid Temptation Situations?

To answer this question, the author wants to be more specific with his suggestion. He begins this chapter by explaining that the fear which keeps us smoking has two distinct phases.

The first phase consists of panic. This usually happens when a person who is dependent on nicotine realizes that he is running out of cigarette, but there are no stores anywhere in sight. According to the author, this panic isn't caused by withdrawal pangs; instead, it is due to a psychological fear of dependency. And fortunately, the fact that it is psychological should make you less worried about your situation. Trust this method and you will soon break free of this fear.

On the other hand, the second phase involves the fear of an unenjoyable future. To some smokers, they think that living without cigarette is a miserable life. They fear that they can no longer cope with trauma, or that they could no longer relax. However, this is all just part of nicotine's brainwashing. Once they are free, they will soon realize that the opposite is true.

Now that we have identified the two phases of fear, the author wants to discuss the two main categories of temptation avoidance.

- Some smokers avoid smoking, but keep a stash of cigarette within their reach because they claim to gain a confidence boost by simply knowing that they're there. Unfortunately, this method guarantees a higher rate of failure, compared to those who commit to completely discarding their cigarettes.

  The author explains that the essential requirements in order to succeed with his method are certainty and a positive mindset. Having a positive mindset will not be enough, especially if the person is not committed to his goal.

- The second category of temptation avoidance includes situations. According to the author, it would be best for us to avoid stressful situations, but go out and enjoy social events. He goes on to add that putting ourselves in stressful situations wouldn't solve anything while, on the other hand, attending social events will help us enjoy the occasion. This will make us realize that we do not need nicotine in order to enjoy a party. And while you're at it, make sure to rejoice over the fact that you are another step closer to your goal.

The Moment of Revelation

About three weeks after a smoker puts out his final cigarette, he will be able to experience his moment of revelation. According to the author, this moment is the most beautiful part, since you no longer have to remind yourself that there is no need to smoke. And the best part about this moment is that it has a lasting effect, which guarantees that we would no longer be tempted to light another stick of cigarette.

But this doesn't mean that all of us would take three weeks to experience this moment. Depending on how committed a person is, he can either expect it to happen immediately or within a few months.

However, the author also wants to make it clear that the moment of revelation isn't something you patiently wait for day in and day out. Instead of just waiting for this magical moment, go out and enjoy everything that life has to offer. Don't sit around and worry that your moment of revelation hasn't arrived yet. Relax. Have fun. One day, you'll just wake up and realize that you've finally broken the chain.

The Final Cigarette

In a previous chapter, the author asks us to delay smoking until the end of this book. With everything discussed up until now, he acknowledges that we are now ready to smoke that final cigarette.

But before doing so, he wants us to make sure of the following:

- That we are certain and determined to reach our goal.

- That we are experiencing a sense of excitement over the fact that we are finally going to be free from the bonds of nicotine slavery.

Don't hesitate to take your time and assess your current situation. If you have doubts, then you're free to re-read this entire book. After all, you must be absolutely certain that you are ready to quit smoking, otherwise you'll keep falling back into the trap.

On the other hand, if you're already certain of success, the author simply wants us to follow these instructions:

1. Make a vow to completely give up smoking, and take that vow to heart.

2. As you smoke that last cigarette, do so consciously. Let the filth from the smoke fill your lungs with every puff you take, and ask yourself whether this is something you really find pleasurable.

3. When you finally extinguish that last cigarette, embrace the feeling of freedom. Focus on how great it feels to be free from your nicotine slavery.

4. For around three weeks, you will experience cravings. This is a sign that the nicotine is finally exiting your body, so the nicotine monster is trying to lure you into taking another cigarette. During these times, the author wants us to focus on rejoicing that we are finally going to succeed in our mission to be a non-smoker.

5. And finally, we must continuously remind ourselves that we made the right decision. Doubting our decision to quit will only make us feel miserable, and as a result, would tempt us into lighting another cigarette.

If we carefully follow the abovecited instructions, then the author guarantees that we can finally say goodbye to smoking. To conclude this chapter, the author also wants to share the following tips:

- It's worth reiterating that we should never doubt our decision.

- Don't wait to become a non-smoker; instead, choose to be one now.

- The moment of revelation will just happen. Don't waste your life away by waiting for that moment.

- Avoid using substitutes at all costs.

- When you see smokers, pity them because they are slaves to nicotine.

- Bad days happen to everyone – and a quick smoking break doesn't make a bad day become better.

- Whenever you feel the urge to smoke, remind yourself to rejoice over the fact that you are already a non-smoker today.

A Final Warning

Now that we're finally nicotine-free, we now have a fresh perspective on smoking. However, we shouldn't stop here.

According to the author, no matter how sure we are that we won't fall into the trap again, we must make a commitment to never smoke another cigarette. After all, our addiction began with only one cigarette.

To warn us against falling into the nicotine trap again, the author wants us to remember these simple reminders:

- Cigarette does nothing for us. Not only is it bad for our health, but it also promotes an antisocial behavior.

- Try to think of the horrible experience you had during the withdrawal period. Do you really want to experience the suffering all over again?

Feedback

The author has been advocating the Easy Way to stop smoking for over twenty years now. During this time, he has gathered enough information as to why it works and why others still have a hard time with this method.

To guarantee success with this method, the author was able to come up with a checklist to make the process easier for us. The checklist is as follows:

1. We should make a vow to never intoxicate yourself with nicotine – whether it be smoking, chewing, or sucking. But more importantly, we should stick to this vow and take it to heart.

2. Keep on reminding yourself that you're not giving up anything. Smoking offers no disadvantages, and neither does it provide us with genuine pleasure. It is merely a prop which we can get rid of whenever we choose to.

3. There is no such thing as a smoker who can't quit. All smokers fell for the same trap, and all of them can escape it.

4. If you're having doubts about your decision to quit, remind yourself of the cons of smoking vis-à-vis its

pros, if any. This will make you realize that you made the right decision, since there really is nothing to gain from smoking.

5. Don't avoid the thought of smoking. If it crosses your mind form time to time, rejoice over the fact that you are no longer a smoker.

6. Do not:

   a. Resort to using nicotine substitutes like gums or nasal sprays.

   b. Hesitate on throwing away all your packs of cigarettes.

   c. Avoid smokers.

   d. Drastically change your lifestyle just because you stopped smoking.

7. And finally, don't want for the moment of revelation to happen. Just go with how life flows, and one day you'll just realize that you're already free from the bonds of the nicotine monster.

Help the Smoker Left on the Sinking Ship

It is a known fact that all smokers, if given the chance to quit without being subjected to withdrawal pangs, would give up on smoking in an instant. Unfortunately, only those who are truly committed can make it through the process.

According to the author, the smokers who are left on the sinking ship are the ones who need help more than ever. When they see their friends finally giving up on smoking, they end up feeling hopeless – and as a result, they often turn to intoxicating themselves more with nicotine. More than ever, now is the time for ex-smokers to step up and help improve the lives of others.

Thus, those who successfully make it through the withdrawal stage have the duty to help other smokers get through this phase. Remind them that their fears are all psychological, and that withdrawal symptoms are all in their heads. But more importantly, we must remind them of the benefits of quitting, and how easy it is to break free.

After all, only a fellow smoker would know the struggle; and there could be no better source of inspiration than one who has successfully extinguished his last cigarette.

Advice to Non-smokers

As soon as you experience the moment of revelation, you would immediately want to tell the whole world about it – especially your friends who seem to have given up on quitting. However, the author advices that forcing a smoker to try the Easy Way isn't the best thing to do.

Instead, he advises us to surround the smoker with ex-smokers first. When he is constantly surrounded by people who successfully stopped smoking, the smoker can find inspiration and strength to do so himself. In contrast, if we try to force him to stop smoking immediately, he would end up feeling trapped, and that can only make his nicotine addiction worse. Allow him to open up to the idea of quitting in his own time.

Once he is finally ready to take the final cigarette, which would be the perfect time to make him read this book. He will find this new approach more refreshing – after all, other books filled with pictures and information on lung diseases couldn't possibly be inspiring.

During the withdrawal period, your friend will be overwhelmed by a variety of emotions. This can cause him to be irritable at times. When this happens, the author wants us to be more understanding about his situation. Instead, we should shower them with praises about their progress. And soon enough, they too will experience the moment of revelation.

Conclusion

Smokers all over the world can agree that quitting is never easy. Despite the various methods claiming to help smokers change their ways, none of them proved to be a hundred percent effective. That is – until Allen Carr's Easy Way came along.

In this books, Allen Carr details the method he used to overcome his chain-smoking habits. According to him, there are only two important steps: to commit and to keep a positive mindset.

To commit means to make a vow to finally put an end to smoking. But most importantly, we must promise to take that vow to heart. However, committing to this promise can take a toll on us, and that's when the second step comes along. This situation is particularly true during the withdrawal period.

According to the author, when we are tempted to light up a cigarette, we shouldn't allow ourselves to feel deprived. Instead, we should focus on the fact we are only being tempted because we are no longer doing that nasty habit. We should focus on the fact that we have already decided to quit, and rejoice every moment that we remain free from nicotine slavery.

Nonetheless, maintaining this mindset doesn't mean that we always have to avoid social events. The author wants to make it clear that quitting doesn't involve a drastic change in the way we live. Instead of avoiding social events, he wants us to enjoy them. This will help us realize that we don't need cigarettes in order to be confident and sociable. And when we hear the nicotine monster asking for just one puff, rejoice over the fact that you are now in control of your life, and are no longer giving in to the requests of the monster.

Aside from social events, there are also other instances when our rejoicing mindset would be tested. These can include hanging out with fellow smokers, or simply watching a TV show where a character coolly lights a cigarette. Again, we must focus on the fact that we are no longer chained to the little monster in our head. We must always remind ourselves that we are only experiencing these temptations because the monster is starving, and is desperate for a taste.

Fortunately, studies reveal that it only takes around three weeks for our body to get rid of all the nicotine. This means that, on average, the withdrawal period only lasts for three weeks.

Soon enough, we will finally be able to experience the moment of revelation. The author describes this as the liberating feeling of knowing that we are no longer under the control of the little monster. He wants us to remember, however, that this feeling is not something that we have to wait for. Instead, it is something that just happens when we least expect it to happen.

To conclude, as long as we know how to follow a clear set of instructions, then we are already bound to succeed with the Easy Way. With nothing to give up and everything to gain, there is no reason for us to keep on delaying our plan to finally stop smoking.

Final Thoughts

Hey! Did you enjoy this book? We sincerely hope you thoroughly enjoyed this short read and have gotten immensely valuable insights that will help you in any areas of your life.

Would it be too greedy if we ask for a review from you?

It takes 1 minute to leave 1 review to possibly influence 1 more person's decision to read just 1 book which may change their 1 life. Your 1 minute matters and we value it and thank you so much for giving us your 1 minute. If it sucks, just say it sucks. Period.

FREE BONUS

P.S. Is it okay if we overdeliver?

Here at Abbey Beathan Publishing, we believe in overdelivering way beyond our reader's expectations. Is it okay if we overdeliver?

Here's the deal, we're going to give you an extremely valuable cheatsheet of "Accelerated Learning". We've partnered up with Ikigai Publishing to present to you the exclusive bonus of "Accelerated Learning Cheatsheet"

What's the catch? We need to trust you… You see, we want to overdeliver and in order for us to do that, we've to trust our reader to keep this bonus a secret to themselves. Why? Because we don't want people to be getting our exclusive accelerated learning cheatsheet without even buying our books itself. Unethical, right?

Ok. Are you ready?

Simply Visit this link: http://bit.ly/acceleratedcheatsheet

We hope you'll enjoy our free bonuses as much as we've enjoyed preparing it for you!

Free Bonus #2: Free Book Preview of

Summary: Crushing It!

The Book at a Glance

Gary Vaynerchuk wrote Crushing It as a follow-up to his highly-acclaimed first book called Crush It. In the first book, he laid the foundation for the techniques and strategies that he used to build his own personal brand. He explained how he transformed a local liquor store into a multi-million dollar national operation. In this follow-up book, Vaynerchuk breaks down the strategies based on the most popular social networking platforms during the last few years namely Musical.ly, Snapchat, Twitter, YouTube, Facebook, Instagram, podcasts, and voice-first applications. Furthermore, for every chapter in the book, Vaynerchuk tells true stories of entrepreneurs who successfully implemented the principles he discussed in the first book.

Without further ado, here's a quick overview of the content that you should expect from this branding and business book:

Chapter 1: The reign of traditional marketing is over. Gone are the days wherein only the big corporations have the ability to reach out to legions of customers through marketing campaigns on television, radio, and newspapers. Even if you are just starting out as an entrepreneur, you have the same chances as the multi-national companies out there. If you can build an interesting personal brand, you can crush it in whatever business you want to enter.

Chapter 2: To build a profitable business around your personal brand, you need to focus on the things that really matter. In the words of Vaynerchuk, these are intent, authenticity, passion, patience, speed, work, and attention.

Chapter 3: Everything boils down to the quality of your content. If you offer unique content, people will follow you and pay attention to your every move. If you are offering the same content as everybody else, then you are pushing yourself down.

Chapter 4: Don't let anything stop you from pursuing your passion and making a business out of it. You have to deal with what Vaynerchuk refers to as the three fears: fear of failure, fear of wasting time, and fear of seeming vain.

Chapter 5: Vaynerchuk offers Pat Flynn as the perfect example of a guy who pursued his passion like crazy and emerged a very successful and rich man. Flynn is the man behind the very popular blog called Smart Passive Income.

70

Flynn uses the blog to talk about the various successful online businesses he had built during the years.

Chapter 6: According to Vaynerchuk, the first thing you should do in building your personal brand is to create a Facebook page. Chances are most of your potential audiences are in Facebook. This alone should convince you to start being active on Facebook.

Chapter 7: To be discovered online, you have to be a dogged self-promoter. No one is going to promote yourself so you should might as well do it. This is especially true if you are just starting out. As your brand gets bigger, your followers will start promoting you. But this doesn't mean you should stop putting your name out there.

Chapter 8 to 15: Vaynerchuk goes in-depth in explaining the strategies you should follow in using the largest social media platforms out there namely Musical.ly, Snapchat, Twitter, YouTube, Facebook, Instagram, Podcasting, and voice-first technologies. If you really want to take your personal brand and business to the next level, these are the platforms you should be spending your time and resources on.

Introduction

We are now in a world where an eight-year-old kid and his dad can make thousands of dollars a week just by opening boxes of toys on YouTube. According to Vaynerchuk, this is the kind of world we live in right now. If you have the passion and the hustle for something, you can achieve almost anything you want. Vaynerchuk was lucky enough to have seen the trend during its early days and capitalized on it at full speed. He grew his family's $4 million liquor store into a $60 million business within the span of just a few years. How did he do it? He used as leverage all the tools and resources that the internet and technology have to offer. He created a personal brand and used it to grow his core business.

Now, Vaynerchuk divides his time between his wine business, his digital media company, and several other business projects. His operations now have offices in several cities including Los Angeles, New York City, Chattanooga, and London. He still takes the time to connect and engage with his followers on various social media sites like Twitter, Instagram, Facebook, and Snapchat. He's as busy as ever. He runs a YouTube show where he answers questions from fans. He maintains a daily video documentary. He plays a role in a television reality show called Planet of the Apps. And he's writing books in between.

Since his first book, Crush It, a lot has changed. This is why Vaynerchuk wrote a second book to expand on the topics he has discussed in the first book. He wants to update his readers about the latest information and developments on how to leverage internet platforms to create a lasting and powerful personal brand. The main difference between the first book and this one is that this one includes voices from other entrepreneurs who have achieved the same level of success as Vaynerchuk. These are entrepreneurs who achieved success by implementing the principles and concepts discussed in the first book.

A lot of entrepreneurs became successful after following the advice on Crush It. There's John Lee Dumas who started his own business podcast which now generates $200,000 a month. There's Louie Blaka who went from obscure art teacher to a thriving artist who now sells his paintings with price tags reaching up to five figures. He also hosts painting events that can attract a hundred people per event. These two successful entrepreneurs are just a few of the hundreds of people who achieved their goals after reading Crush It.

Chapter 1: The Path Is All Yours

Influencer marketing is quickly taking over traditional marketing. There's a reason why more and more companies are targeting online audiences instead of pumping money into television and print advertisements. Traditional marketing is on a downturn while online marketing continues to evolve as a powerful platform. Just think about it. More than a billion cumulative hours are spent every day on YouTube by its users. The average person spends at least one hour on Facebook every day. Around 4,000 videos and photos are posted on Instagram every hour. Needless to say, there's a changing of the guard here. In with the new and out with the old.

Since 2009, big brands have tripled the amount of money they spend on advertising that targets online audiences. Billions of dollars are being pumped into online platforms like social networking sites, blogs, forums, and applications. This is where you can get in with your own personal brand and get a piece of the pie. Being an influences in any niche can be very lucrative. There are brands out there who are more than willing to pay you top dollar just by posting a photo on Twitter or Facebook or Instagram. How legitimate is influencer marketing, you may ask. Well, it's legitimate enough that in 2016 alone, the top personalities on YouTube got paid $70 million.

Building yourself to be an influencer takes time. The steps you need to take to get to that point was discussed in detail by Vaynerchuk in his first book, Crush It. In the simplest of terms, an influencer is someone who builds an online audience which is big enough that brands are willing to pay him money if he posts a link, a story, a video, or a photo about their products and services. Have you ever come across a YouTube video wherein the person talks about a product or a service right after his core content? That's the most basic example of an online personality being paid to mention a brand's product or service. This is often referred to in the marketing industry as product placement. A lot of YouTubers make most of their money through these product placements.

Personal Brands Are For Everyone

Many people have the wrong assumption that personal brands are only applicable for creative types of people like artists, photographers, and musicians. It's true that a lot of those who were able to successfully monetize their personal brands are composed by these creative types. But that doesn't mean they are the only ones who can do it. Again, if you are passionate about something and you are willing to toil to create your personal brand, you can easily achieve what they have achieved. It doesn't matter where your passion lies. It can be about beekeeping or mountain climbing or stamp collecting. If you are good at it and you are passionate about it, there's absolutely no reason why you can't monetize it.

How I'm Crushing It: Amy Schmittauer, Savvy Sexy Social

Amy's rise as an online celebrity came as an accident. A video she made for a friend's wedding ceremony made her realize that she can tell stories that resonate with a lot of people. While working full-time at a law firm, Amy also worked part-time as a social media manager. She was contented with what she was making until she read Vaynerchuk's first book, Crush It. She realized that she was worth much more so she quit her job and focused on building her own personal brand. Her earnings and reputation quickly grew. She now runs a video channel with nearly 100,000 subscribers. She has written best-selling books, created influential vlogging tutorial series, and presented as a keynote speaker in stages all over the world.

Read More…

SUMMARY

CRUSHING IT!

HOW GREAT ENTREPRENEURS BUILD
THEIR BUSINESS AND INFLUENCE
AND HOW YOU CAN, TOO

BY: GARY VAYNERCHUK

ABBEY BEATHAN

CPSIA information can be obtained
at www.ICGtesting.com
Printed in the USA
LVHW091136240619
622139LV00001B/109/P